EASY PIANO

Contents

ISBN 0-7935-8754-9

Wonderland Music Company, Inc.

DISTRIBUTED BY

7777 W. BLUEMOUND RD. P.O. BOX 13819 MILWAUKEE, WI 53213

Disney characters and artwork © Disney Enterprises, Inc.

Visit Hal Leonard Online at
www.halleonard.com

Winnie the Pooh and the Blustery Day

Winnie the Pooh and the Honey Tree

HEFFALUMPS AND WOOZLES

Words and Music by RICHARD M. SHERMAN
and ROBERT B. SHERMAN

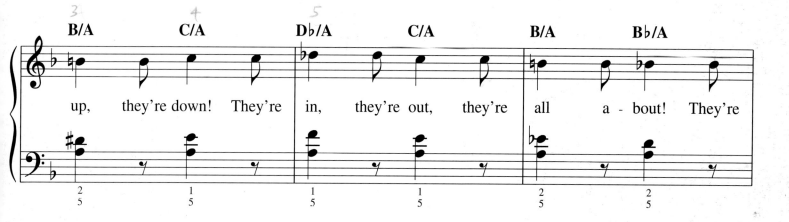

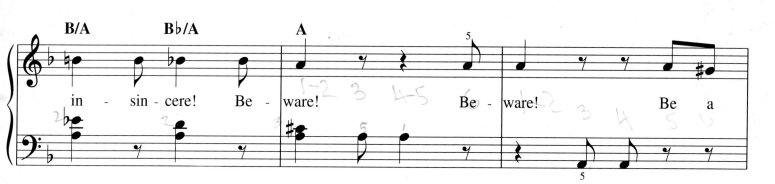

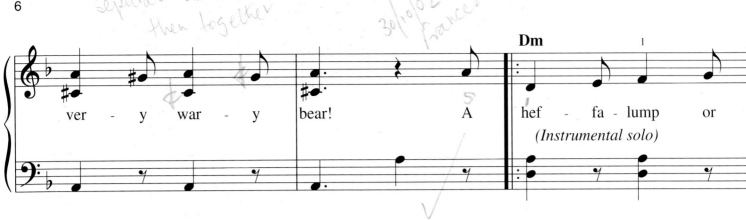

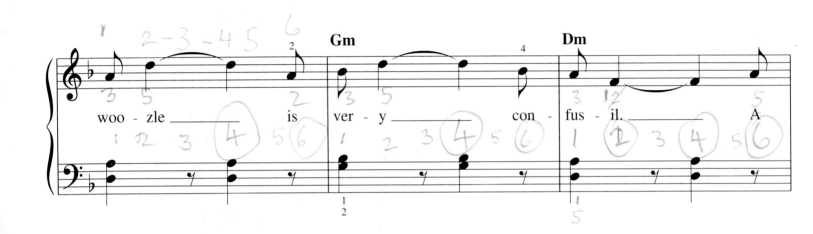

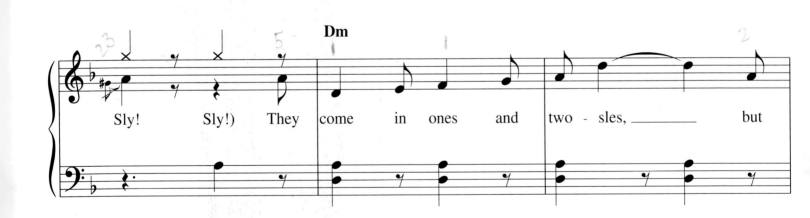

if they _____ so choo - sles, _____ be - fore your eyes you'll

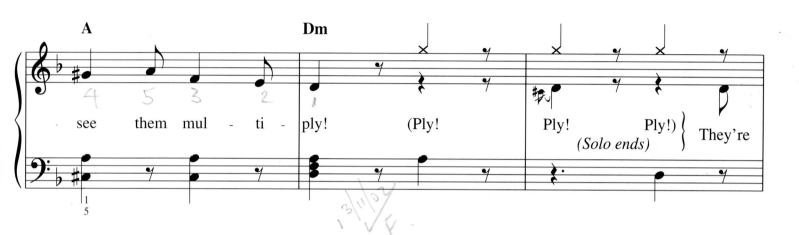

see them mul - ti - ply! (Ply! Ply! Ply!) *(Solo ends)* They're

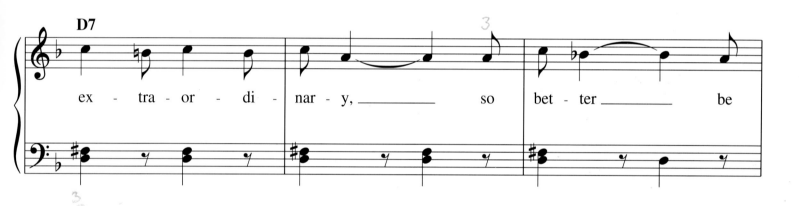

ex - tra - or - di - nar - y, _____ so bet - ter _____ be

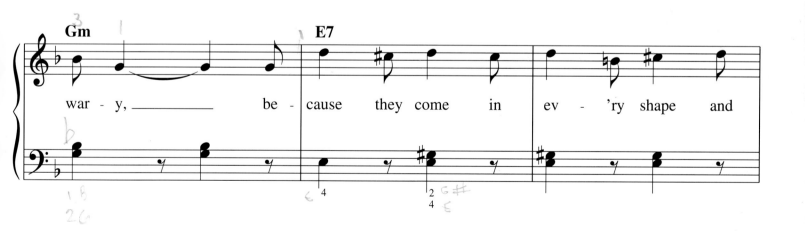

war - y, _____ be - cause they come in ev - 'ry shape and

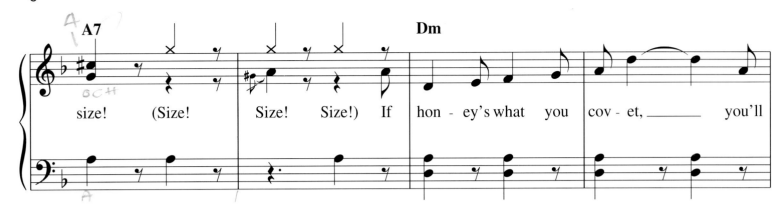

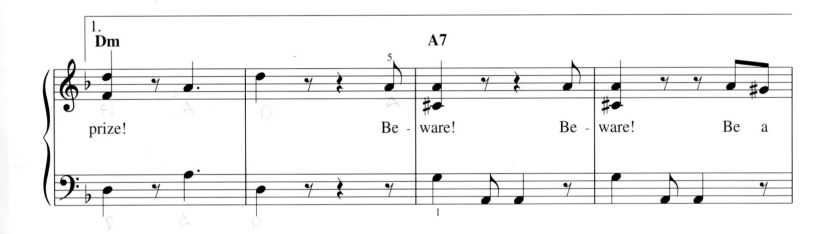

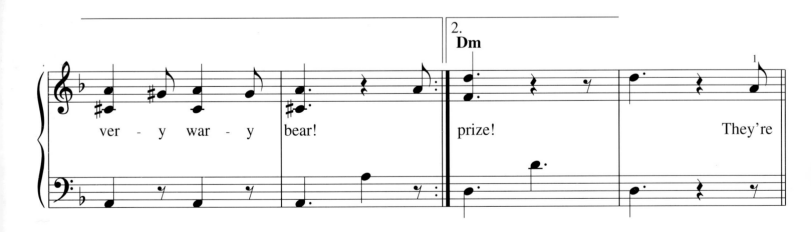

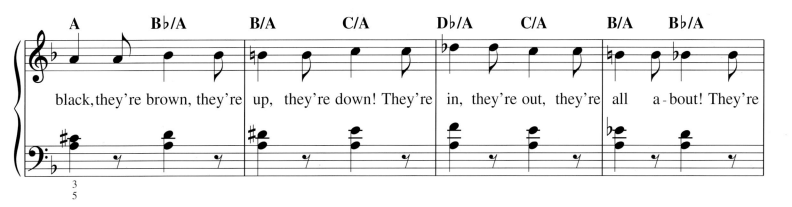

black, they're brown, they're up, they're down! They're in, they're out, they're all a-bout! They're

far, they're near, they're gone, they're here! They're quick, they're slick, they're in - sin-cere! Be -

ware! Be - ware! Be - ware! Be - ware! Be -

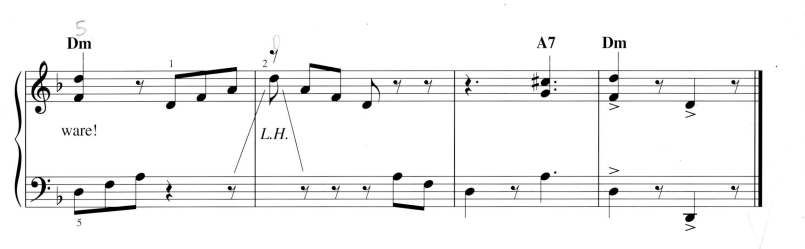

ware!

HIP HIP POOH RAY

Words and Music by RICHARD M. SHERMAN
and ROBERT B. SHERMAN

Festive March

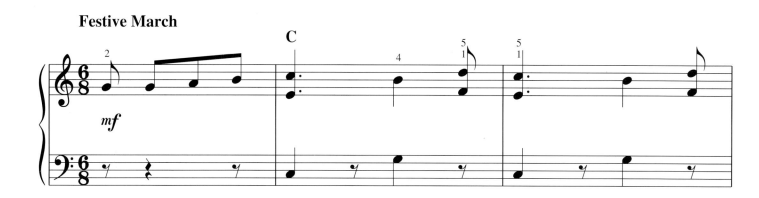

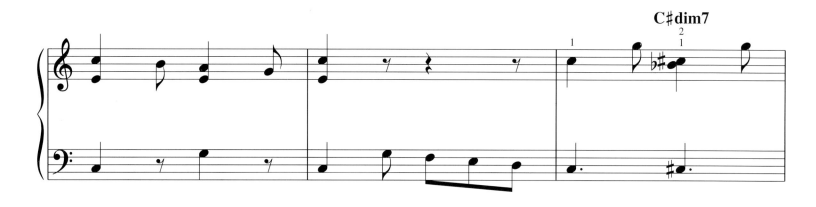

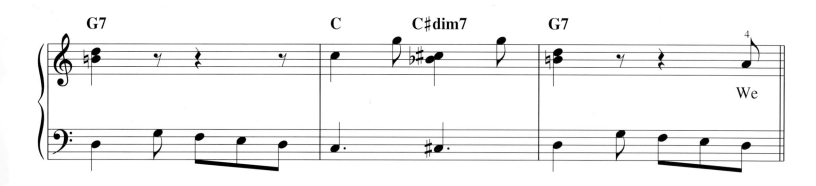

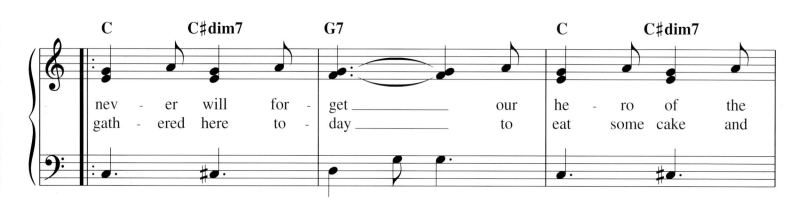

nev - er will for - get _____ our he - ro of the
gath - ered here to - day _____ to eat some cake and

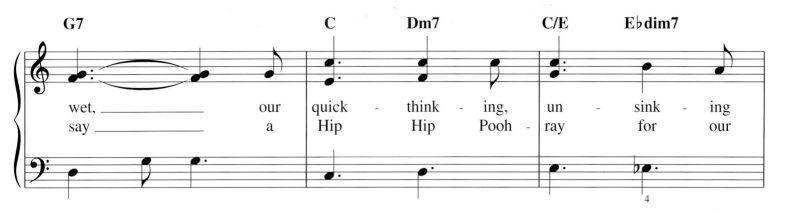

wet, _____ our quick - think - ing, un - sink - ing
say _____ a Hip Hip Pooh - ray for our

Pooh bear! _____ And Pig - let, who in -
he - roes! _____ The stuff of which they're

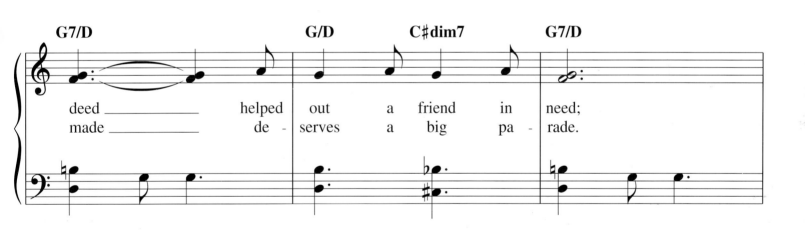

deed _____ helped out a friend in need;
made _____ de - serves a big pa - rade.

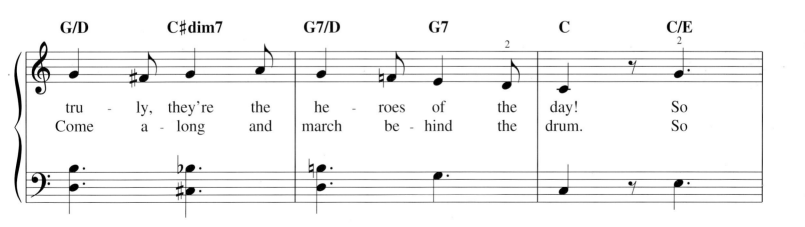

tru - ly, they're the he - roes of the day! So
Come a - long and march be - hind the drum. So

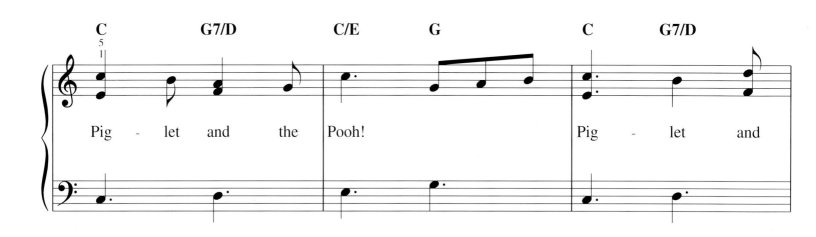

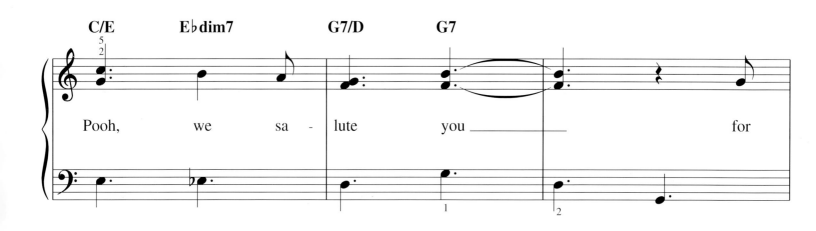

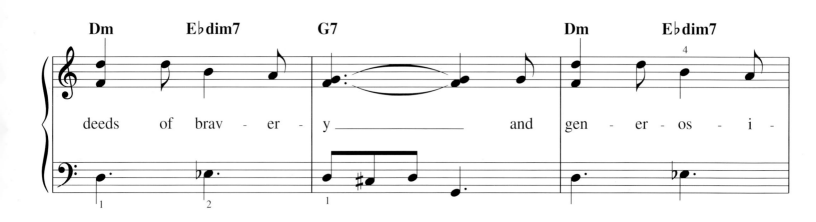

LITTLE BLACK RAIN CLOUD

Words and Music by RICHARD M. SHERMAN
and ROBERT B. SHERMAN

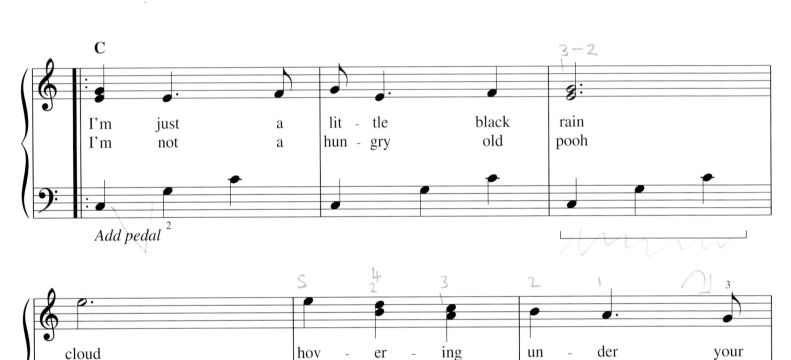

I'm just a lit-tle black rain
I'm just not a hun-gry black old pooh

cloud hov-er-ing un-der your
bear. I'm just a lit-tle your black

hon-ey tree. On-ly a lit-tle black
hon-ey cloud. No one knows bet-ter than

rain
me,

cloud,
bees,

pay no at - ten - tion to
steal - ing your hon - ey is

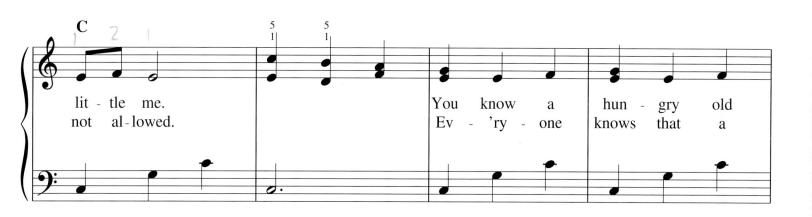

lit - tle me.
not al - lowed.

You know a hun - gry old
Ev - 'ry - one knows that a

pooh
rain

cloud
cloud

does - n't eat
nev - er eats

hon - ey, no,
hon - ey, no,

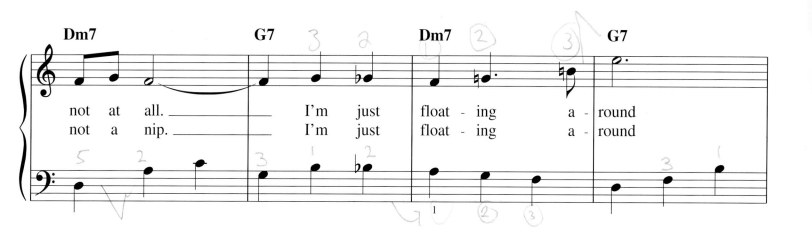

not at all. _____
not a nip. _____

I'm just
I'm just

float - ing a - round
float - ing a - round

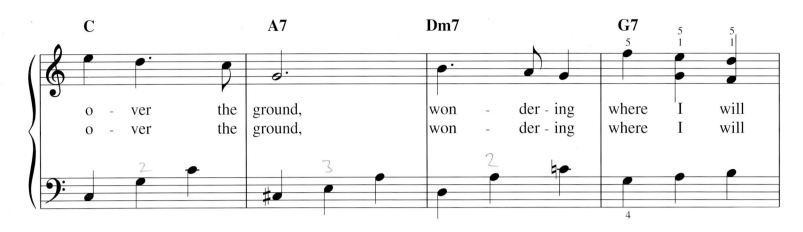

o - ver the ground, won - der - ing where I will
o - ver the ground, won - der - ing where I will

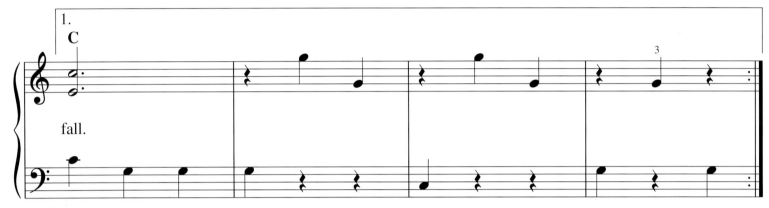

1.

fall.

No pedal

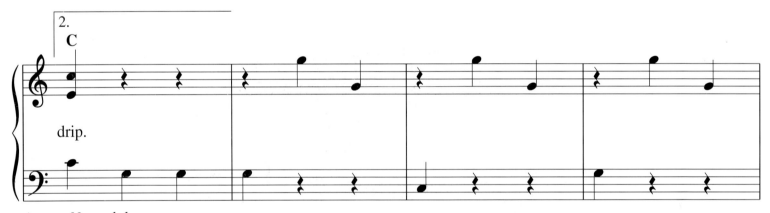

2.

drip.

No pedal

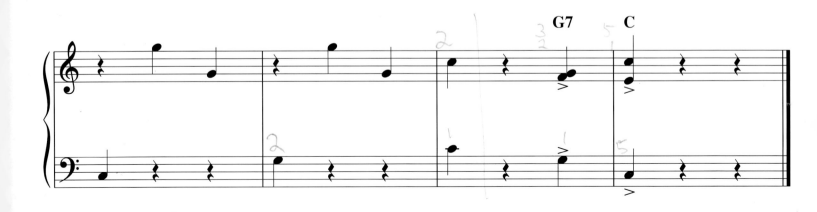

THE RAIN RAIN RAIN CAME DOWN DOWN DOWN

Words and Music by RICHARD M. SHERMAN
and ROBERT B. SHERMAN

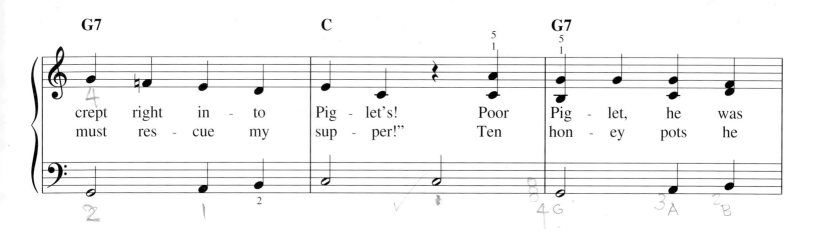

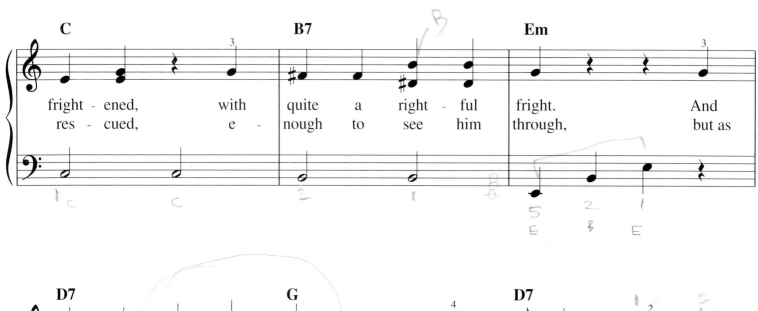

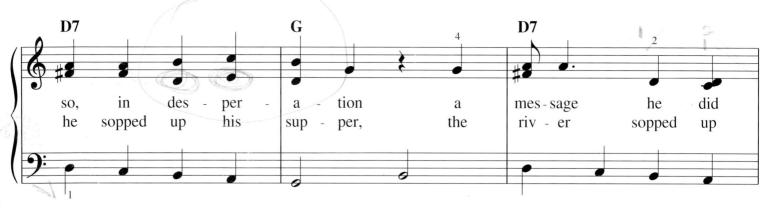

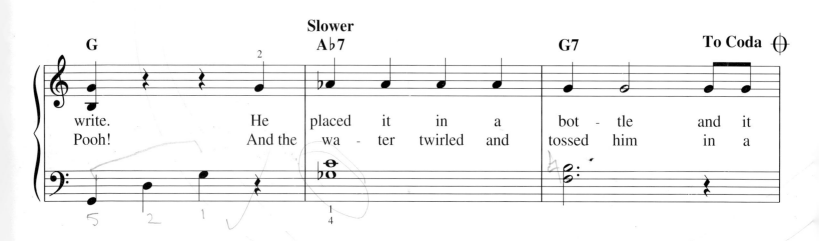

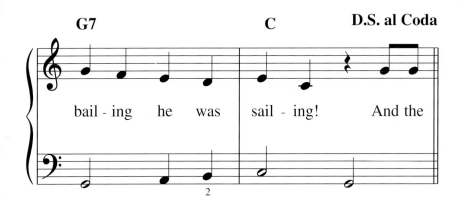

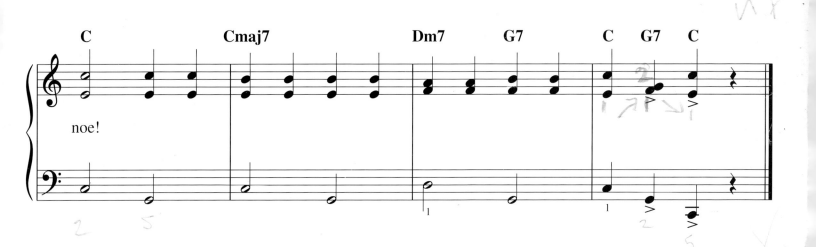

MIND OVER MATTER

Words and Music by RICHARD M. SHERMAN
and ROBERT B. SHERMAN

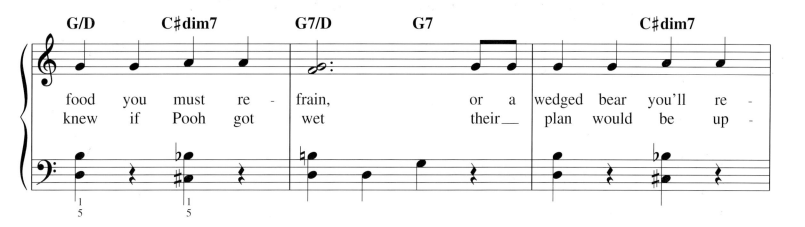

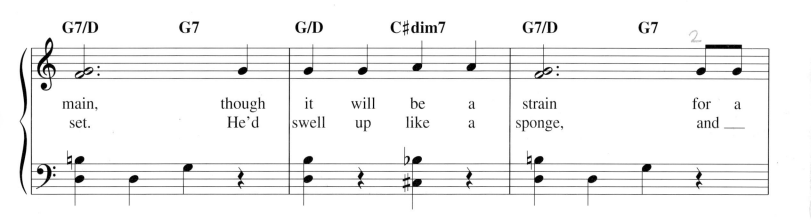

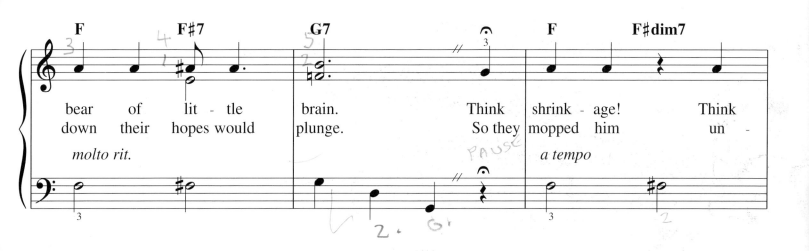

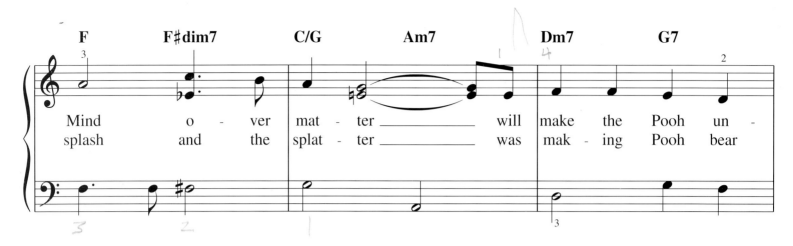

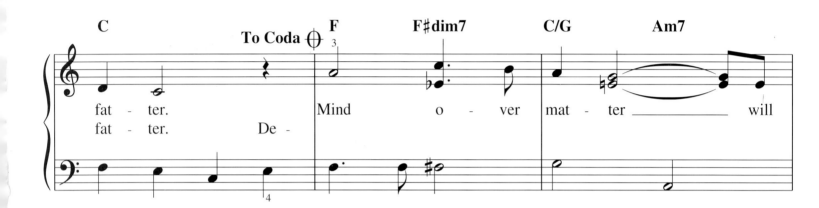

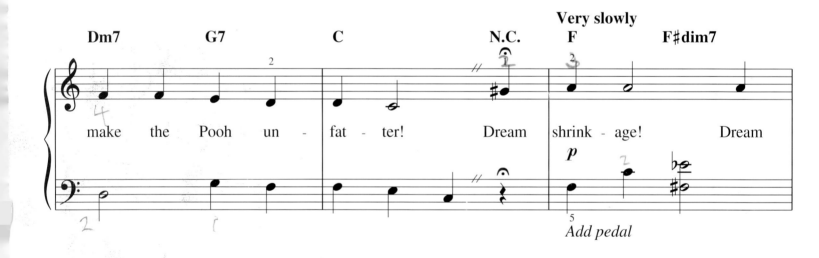

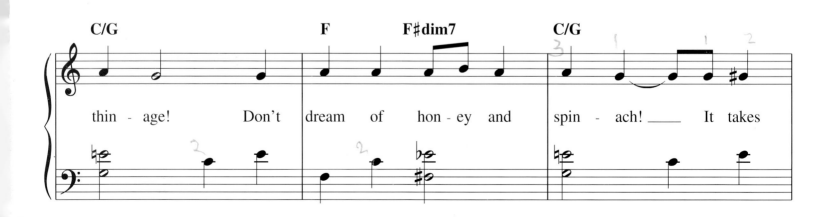

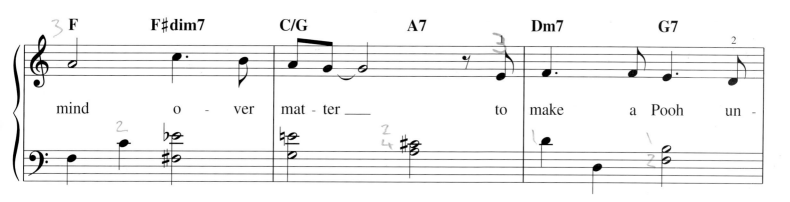

mind   o - ver   mat - ter _____   to   make   a   Pooh   un -

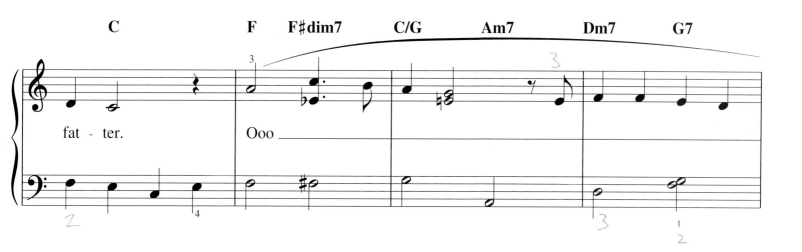

fat - ter.   Ooo _____

Dal Segno

D.S. al Coda

CODA   **Very slowly**

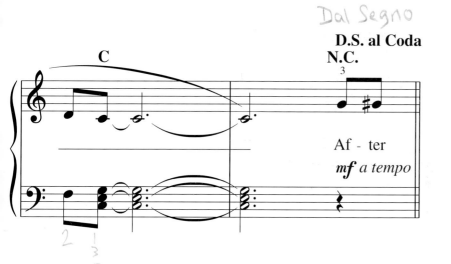

N.C.

Af - ter

mf   *a tempo*

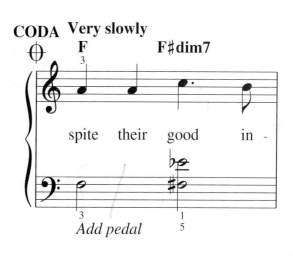

spite   their   good   in -

Add pedal

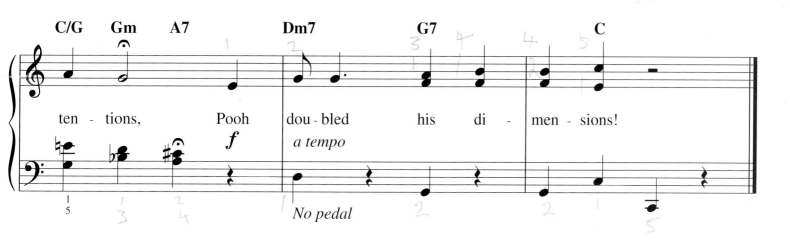

ten - tions,   Pooh   dou - bled   his   di - men - sions!

f   *a tempo*

No pedal

A RATHER BLUSTERY DAY

Words and Music by RICHARD M. SHERMAN
and ROBERT B. SHERMAN

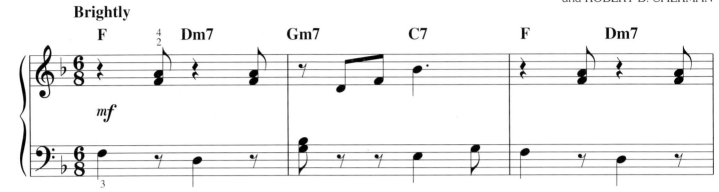

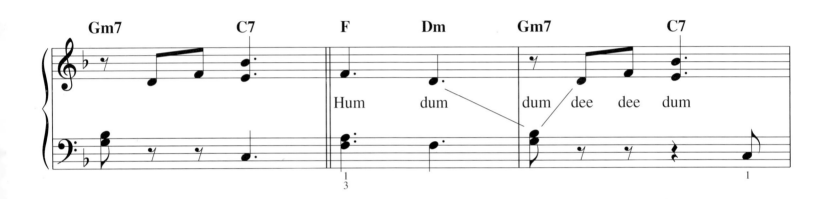

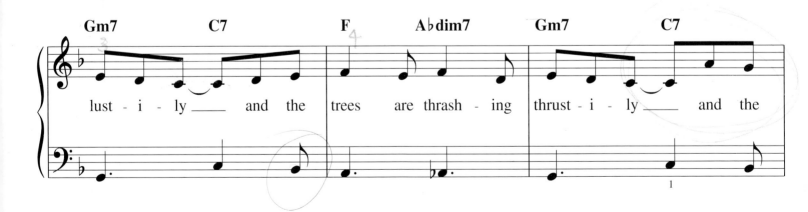

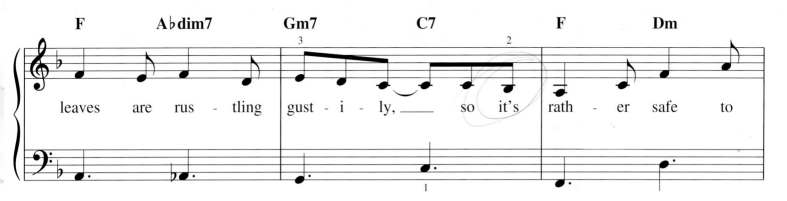

leaves are rus - tling gust - i - ly, _____ so it's rath - er safe to

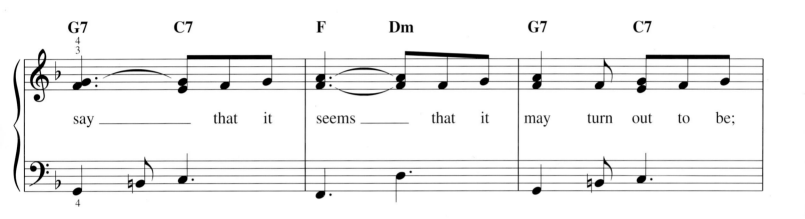

say _____ that it seems _____ that it may turn out to be;

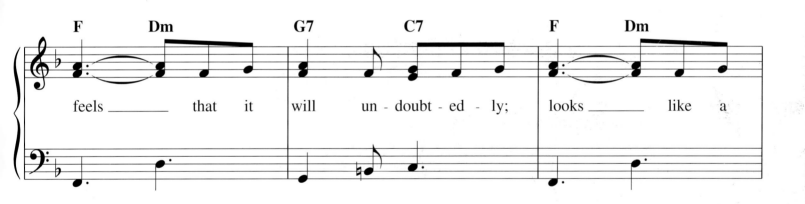

feels _____ that it will un - doubt - ed - ly; looks _____ like a

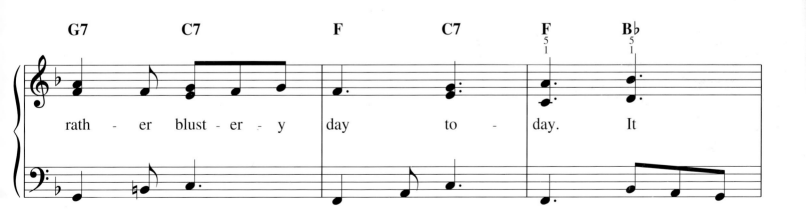

rath - er blust - er - y day to - day. It

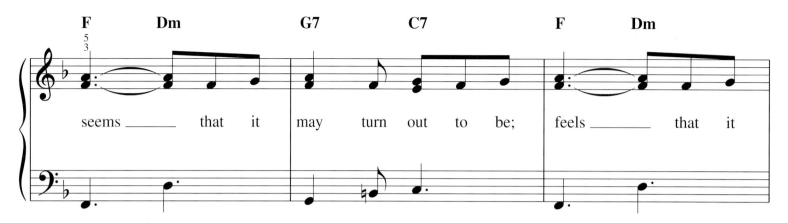

seems _____ that it may turn out to be; feels _____ that it

To Coda ⊕

will un - doubt - ed - ly; looks _____ like a rath - er blust - er - y

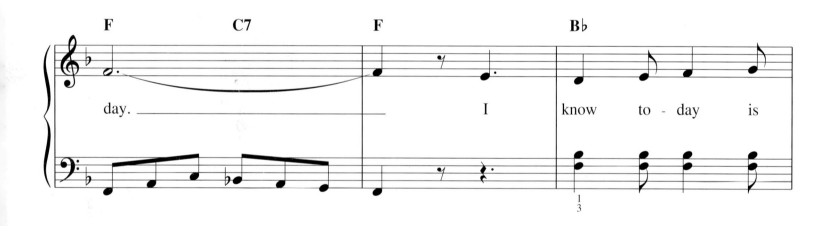

day. _____ I know to - day is

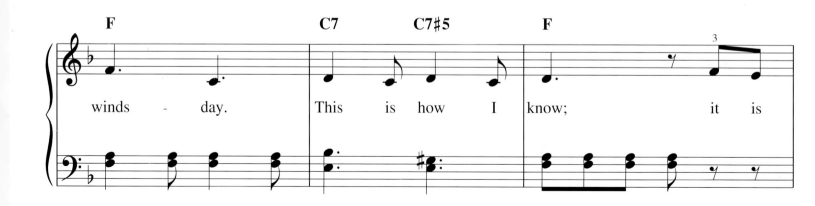

winds - day. This is how I know; it is

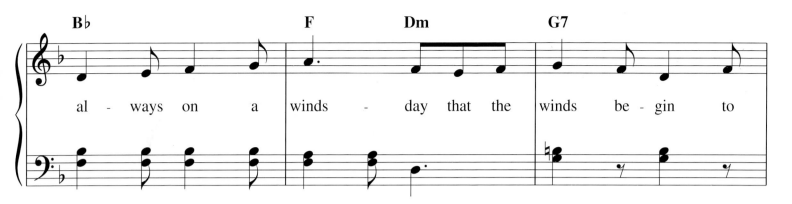

al - ways on a winds - day that the winds be - gin to

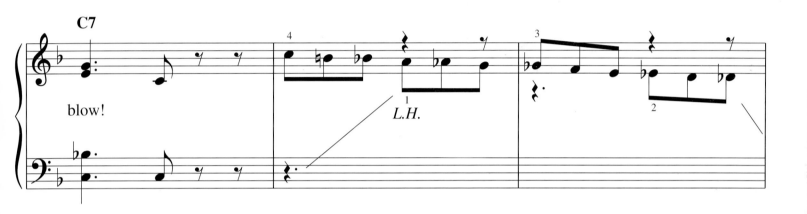

blow! *L.H.*

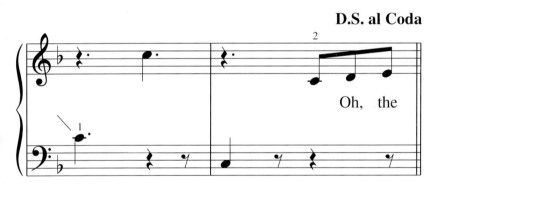

D.S. al Coda

Oh, the

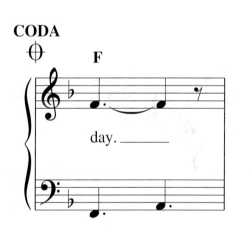

CODA

day. _____

RUMBLY IN MY TUMBLY

Words and Music by RICHARD M. SHERMAN
and ROBERT B. SHERMAN

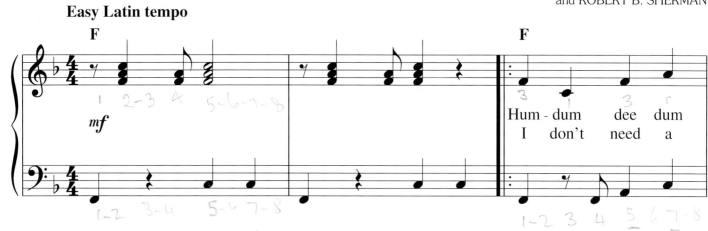

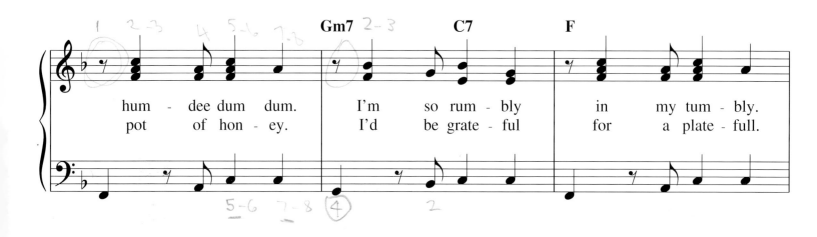

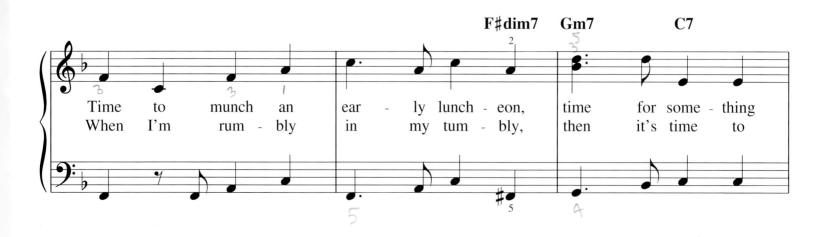

F ... **A7**

sweet!   Oh, I   would - n't   climb   this

eat!   It's the   taste - ful   thing   to

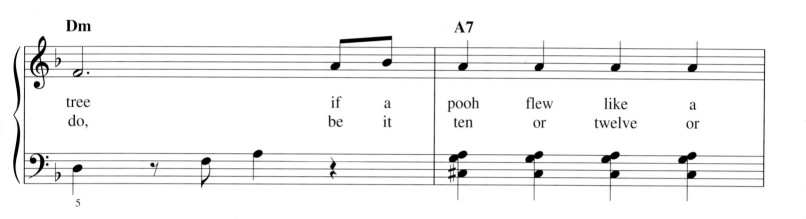

Dm ... **A7**

tree   if   a   pooh   flew   like   a

do,   be   it   ten   or   twelve   or

Dm ... **G7**

bee.   But I   would - n't   be   a

two.   For   an - y - time   is

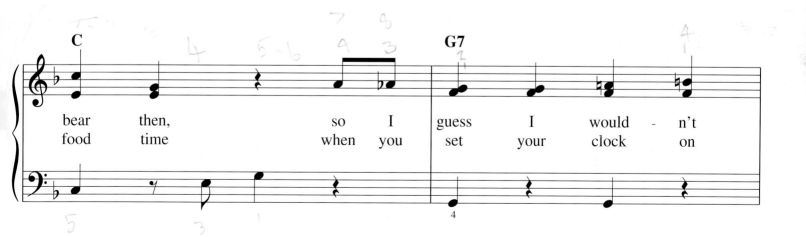

C ... **G7**

bear   then,   so   I   guess   I   would - n't

food   time   when   you   set   your   clock   on

Gm7 C7 F

care then! }
pooh time! }
Bears love hon-ey and I'm a pooh bear,

Gm7 C7 F

so I do care, so I'll climb there. I'm so rum - bly

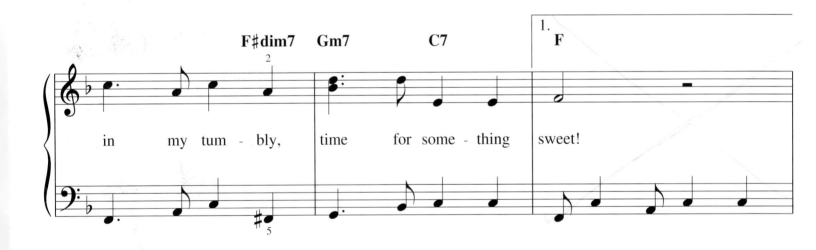

F#dim7 Gm7 C7 1. F

in my tum - bly, time for some - thing sweet!

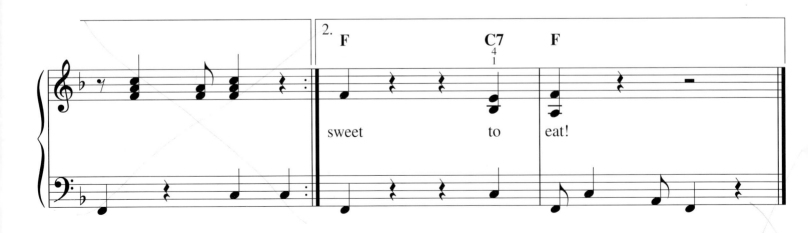

2. F C7 F

sweet to eat!

WINNIE THE POOH

Words and Music by RICHARD M. SHERMAN
and ROBERT B. SHERMAN

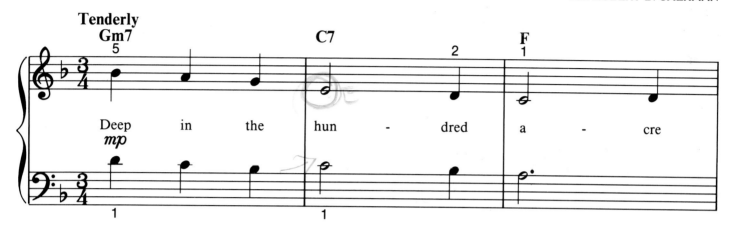

Deep in the hun - dred a - cre

wood where Chris - to - pher Rob - in

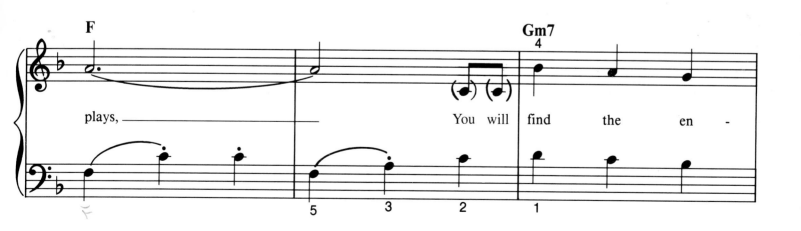

plays, _____ You will find the en -

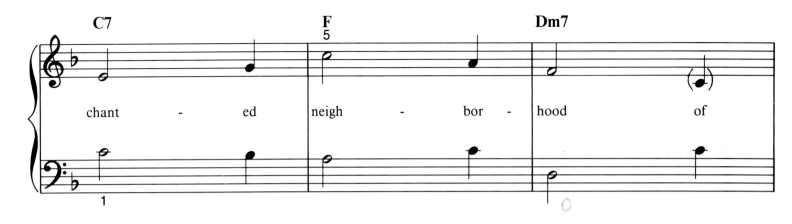

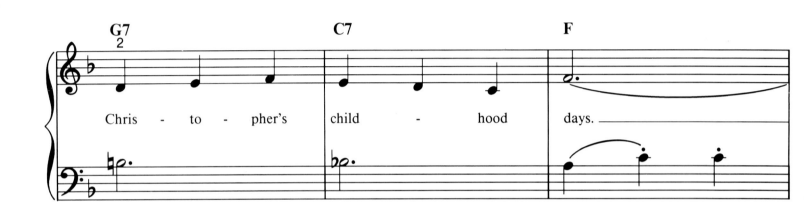

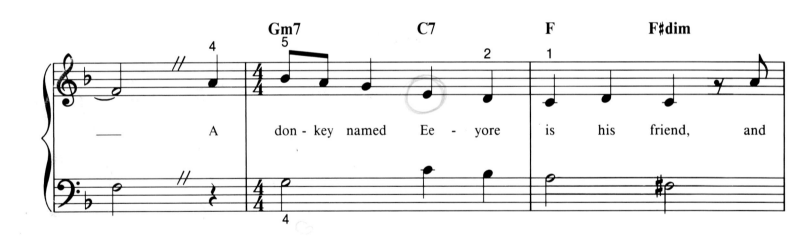

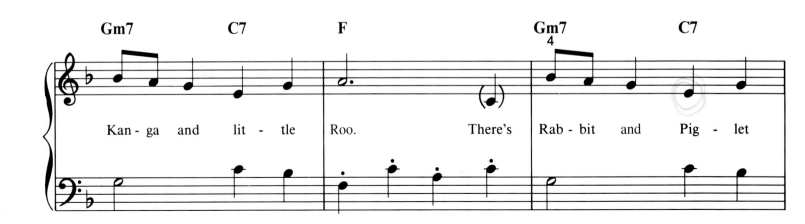

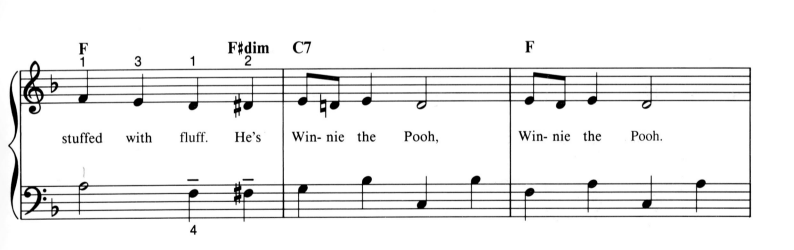

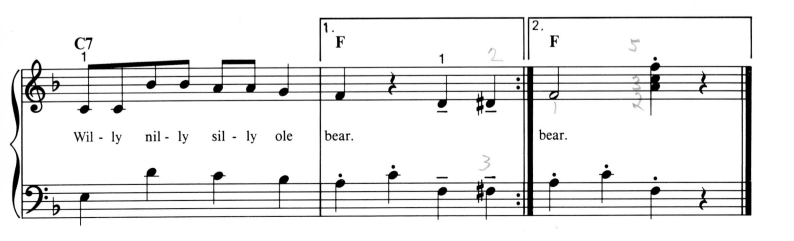

UP, DOWN AND TOUCH THE GROUND

Words and Music by RICHARD M. SHERMAN
and ROBERT B. SHERMAN

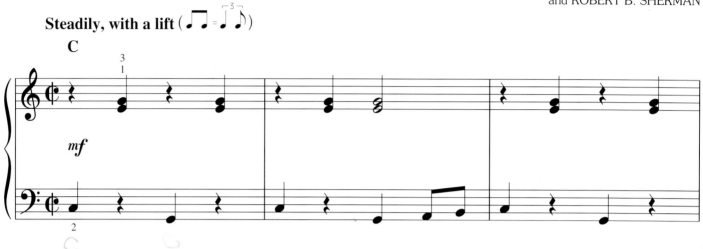

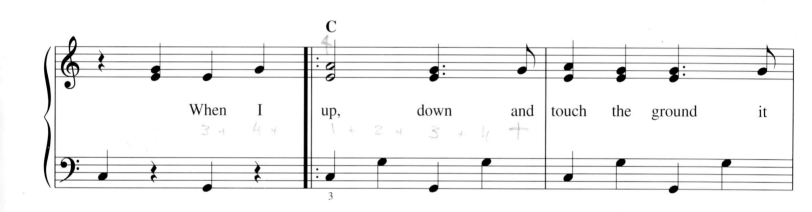

When I up, down and touch the ground it

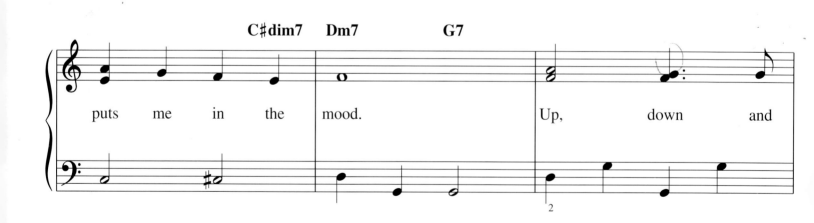

puts me in the mood. Up, down and

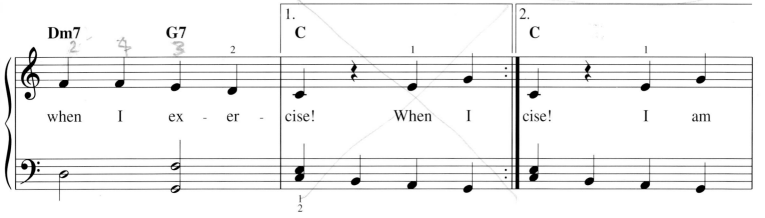

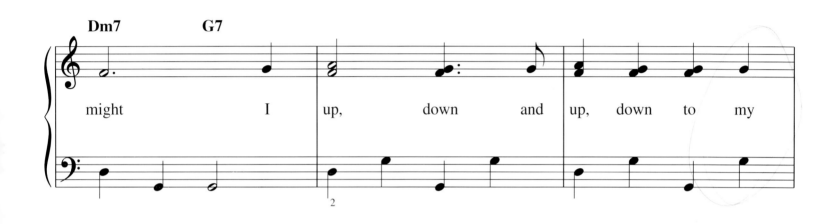

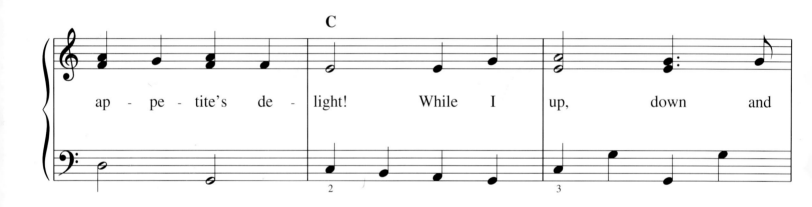

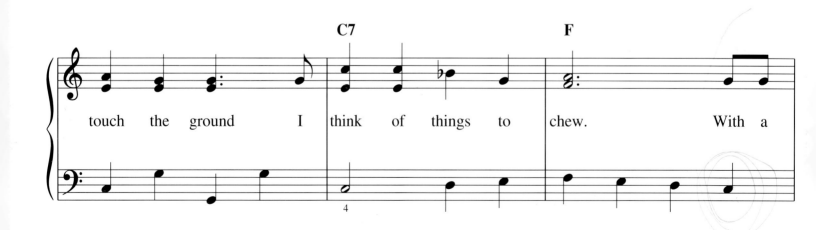

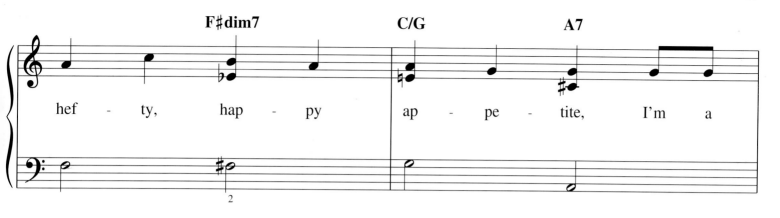

hef - ty, hap - py ap - pe - tite, I'm a

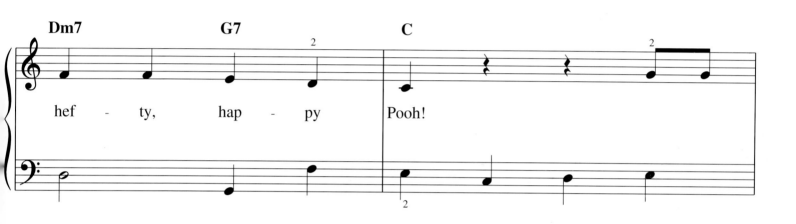

hef - ty, hap - py Pooh!

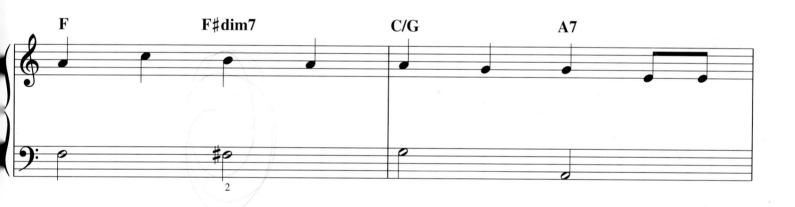

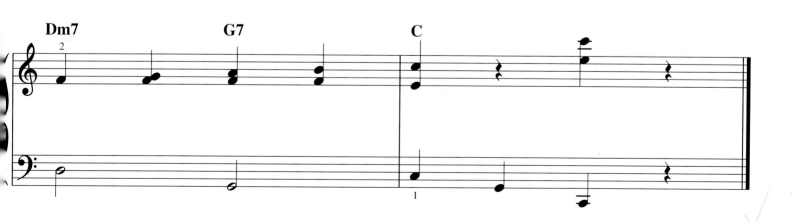

THE WONDERFUL THING ABOUT TIGGERS

Words and Music by RICHARD M. SHERMAN
and ROBERT B. SHERMAN

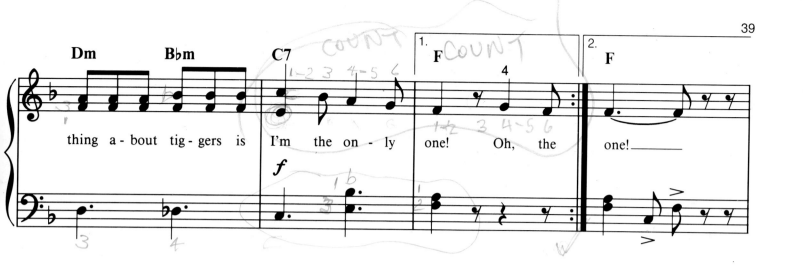

thing a - bout tig - gers is   I'm the on - ly   one! Oh, the   one!_____

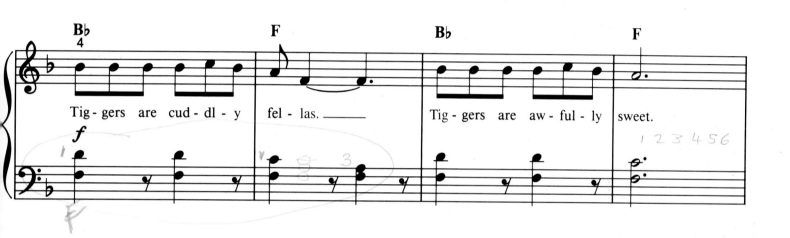

Tig - gers are cud - dl - y   fel - las._____   Tig - gers are aw - ful - ly   sweet.

Ev - 'ry - one else__ is   jea - lous._____   That's why I re - peat and re - peat: The

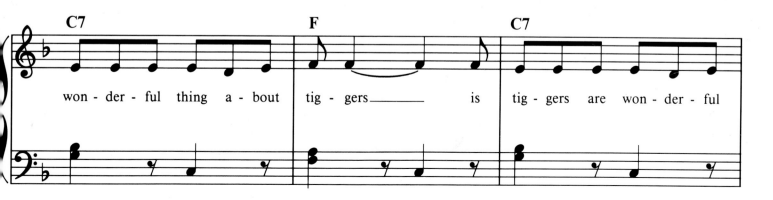

won - der - ful thing a - bout   tig - gers_____   is   tig - gers are won - der - ful

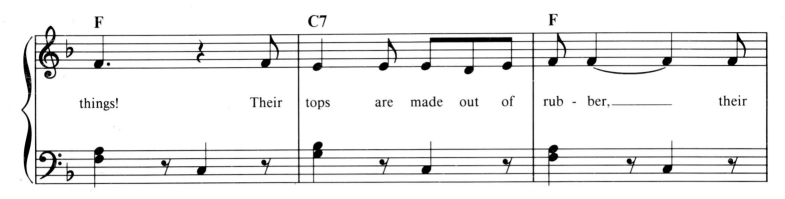

things! Their tops are made out of rub - ber,_____ their

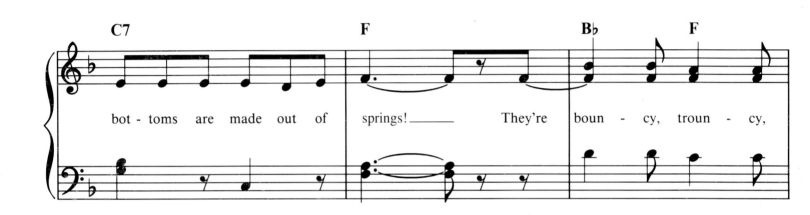

bot - toms are made out of springs!_____ They're boun - cy, troun - cy,

floun - cy, poun - cy, Fun! Fun! Fun! Fun! Fun!_____

But the most won - der - ful thing a - bout tig - gers is I'm the on - ly one!_____